THE MINOTAUR

A one-act drama by
Carol S. Lashof

www.youthplays.com
info@youthplays.com
424-703-5315

COPYRIGHT RULES TO REMEMBER

1. To produce this play, you must receive prior written permission from YouthPLAYS and pay the required royalty.

2. You must pay a royalty each time the play is performed in the presence of audience members outside of the cast and crew. Royalties are due whether or not admission is charged, whether or not the play is presented for profit, for charity or for educational purposes, or whether or not anyone associated with the production is being paid.

3. No changes, including cuts or additions, are permitted to the script without written prior permission from YouthPLAYS.

4. Do not copy this book or any part of it without written permission from YouthPLAYS.

5. Credit to the author and YouthPLAYS are required on all programs and other promotional items associated with this play's performance.

When you pay royalties, you are recognizing the hard work that went into creating the play and making a statement that a play is something of value. We think this is important, and we hope that everyone will do the right thing, thus allowing playwrights to generate income and continue to create wonderful new works for the stage.

Have a question about copyright? Please contact us by email at info@youthplays.com or by phone at 424-703-5315. When in doubt, please ask.

CAST OF CHARACTERS

THE MINOTAUR (Asterion), the youngest child and only living son of the late Queen Pasiphae. He is a boy with the head of a bull.

ARIADNE, a young woman, oldest living child of Queen Pasiphae.

PHAEDRA, a girl, younger daughter of the queen.

KING MINOS, King of Crete, ruler of the Minoan Empire.

THESEUS, a young man, heir to the throne of Athens.

MINOANS, children (including CAENEUS, IASON, MAIA, and PHILOMELE), courtiers, and soldiers.

ATHENIANS, young men and women sent as a sacrifice to Crete.

CHORUS/LABYRINTH

SETTING

The play takes place in about 1500 BCE on the Isle of Crete. Locations are suggested by the ensemble. The action is continuous.

AUTHOR'S NOTE

The play is designed to be performed by an ensemble cast of at least 12, preferably 20-30. All cast members except those playing Ariadne, and The Minotaur double as members of the Chorus.

The playwright wishes to thank director Kate Mendeloff and her actors at Young People's Theater in Ann Arbor, Michigan for their invaluable assistance in developing this script.

(Upstage, ARIADNE and THE MINOTAUR play a game of hide and seek or tag. Their play is at once wild and gentle. Laughing, breathless, they wrestle each other to the ground and pelt each other with leaves. Simultaneously, center stage, the CHORUS begins to "construct" the Labyrinth. They are at once the workers building the labyrinth, the materials from which it is built, and the machines used in the construction. Their movements begin small and gradually become larger. Members of the Chorus repeat the following lines in the manner of a round, softly at first and then louder.)

CHORUS: Set it in stone,
confusion and conflict.
Shame has grown big.
Let the maze hide it.
Like a devious river shifting and winding.
Set it in stone,
confusion and conflict.

(The Chorus reaches a crescendo and then dissolves into a noisy group of boys and girls of the court. Gradually, Ariadne and The Minotaur cease their game to watch the other children, but they stay on the periphery of the action out of sight of the others. Among the children are PHILOMELE, CAENEUS, MAIA, IASON, and PHAEDRA. Phaedra blends in with the group but plays only a passive role in the game that follows – a ritualistic children's game with the children taking turns playing "the monster" and "the hero." The child playing the "monster" stands in the middle of the courtyard pawing the ground like a bull and daring the other young people to come forward to "slay" him.)

Here is a monster, worthy of a hero.
Where is the hero
who will save us from our fears?
Here is the monster.

Where is the hero?
Who will slay him?
Who will save us?

Must we wait for a stranger
to come across the waters?
Or is there one among us
who dares to save us from our fears?

> *(There is a jostling among the children as one is chosen and thrust forward to play the "hero." The "hero" stands in the open and taunts "the monster" while the others form a circle around the antagonists. The first to be chosen as the hero is Philomele, one of the smaller children.)*

Come forth and slay the Minotaur!
Or you'll be eaten for his di-inner!

PHILOMELE: Here I am! I am the hero!

CHORUS: No, you're not, you're only Philomele.

PHILOMELE: Here I am. I'll slay the Minotaur.

CHORUS: No, you won't. He'll send you straight to hell.

> *(After taking her turn as the hero, Philomele becomes the monster and the game continues with a new hero.)*

Come forth and slay the Minotaur!
Or you'll be eaten for his di-inner!

CAENEUS: Here I am! I am the hero!

CHORUS: No, you're not, you're clumsy Caeneus.

CAENEUS: Here I am. I'll slay the Minotaur.

CHORUS: No, you won't. You are a pain-eous.

> *(As the game continues, an older player comes to the fore as the hero and begins throwing pebbles. At first, they are small*

pebbles. The monster dodges most of them, and if any hit home, they do not cause any real pain. Watching the game from a distance, The Minotaur is becoming increasingly agitated. Ariadne whispers to him, evidently attempting to soothe him and to restrain him from approaching the other children.)

Come forth and slay the Minotaur!

MAIA: Here I am! I am the hero!

CHORUS: No, you're not. You're merely Maia.

MAIA: Here I am! I'll slay the Minotaur.

CHORUS: No you won't. You're such a li-ah!

(Iason takes Maia's place as the hero, and she becomes the monster.)

Come forth and slay the Minotaur!
Or you'll be eaten for his di-inner!

IASON: Here I am! I am the hero!

CHORUS: No, you're not. You're stupid Iason.

IASON: Here I am! I'll slay the Minotaur.

(Iason throws a stone hard and straight, hitting Maia who shouts in pain. She tries to break out of the circle, but the other children will not make space for her to come through.)

CHORUS: No you won't. You're such a lazy one!

(As Iason chases Maia around the inside of the circle, The Minotaur breaks away from Ariadne.)

ARIADNE: Asterion, don't!

(The Minotaur darts into the circle of children, replacing Maia in the position of the monster. Maia then joins Iason, throwing stones at The Minotaur.)

IASON AND MAIA: Here I am! I am the hero!
Here I am! I'll slay The Minotaur!

(The other children join in chanting and throwing pebbles. Ariadne tries to break into the circle from outside but cannot.)

ARIADNE: Stop that! Leave him alone!

(The Minotaur lowers his head and charges a weak link in the circle. The circle breaks open and some of the younger children run away. Phaedra slips out of sight but remains onstage. Ariadne approaches her brother and speaks to him.)

Come on. Let's go.

MAIA: Monster-lover!

ARIADNE: Don't call him a monster. He's not a monster.

MAIA: Says you.

ARIADNE: Yes, says me.

MAIA: *(With mocking ingratiation:)* Oh, the princess Ariadne says "Don't call him a monster." Better do as she says. Or else.

CAENEUS: Or else, when she's queen of Crete, she'll make you regret it.

IASON: She'll never be queen of Crete.

MAIA: Queen of the cattle, maybe.

IASON: Queens don't run around in the hills all night with monsters.

PHILOMELE: Phaedra doesn't run around with monsters.

CAENEUS: No, Phaedra just hides in corners and listens to gossip.

PHILOMELE: Everybody listens to gossip. Except maybe you. You want to know what people say about you, Caeneus?

(Philomele whispers something in Caeneus' ear. He gives her a shove. Ariadne takes Asterion by the hand and tries to lead him away.)

IASON: Where are you going, Ariadne? Off to eat grass with your baby brother?

(Iason grabs Ariadne by the arm.)

Why don't you stay and play with us, princess?

THE MINOTAUR: Leave her alone!

MAIA: Oh, how about that? The monster can talk. I thought he could only say "moo." Moo-oo, Moo-oo.

(Several other children join Maia in circling The Minotaur and "mooing" at him.)

IASON: The king should have left him to die when he was a baby. That's what you're supposed to do with monsters. If I was the King —

CAENEUS: If you were the king, I'd feel sorry for Crete. You'd be too stupid to notice how stupid you were.

IASON: I'd be smart enough not to make Poseidon angry. If Poseidon sent me a white bull from the sea —

PHILOMELE: I wish I'd seen the white bull. Everybody says it was the most beautiful creature they've ever seen. And it rose out of the sea covered in foam, and its horns were silver, or maybe pearl.

IASON: No matter how amazing it was, I would have sacrificed it to the gods.

PHILOMELE: Shhh. You shouldn't say things like that.

IASON: I'm only saying that when you don't do what the gods tell you to do...

MAIA: It's true. When the gods give you a gift, you should know how to be grateful. You should make the proper sacrifices. Or maybe you deserve what you get.

CAENEUS: Careful, Maia. If the king heard you...

MAIA: Who's going to tell him?

CAENEUS: Not me.

MAIA: *(To Philomele, threatening:)* How about you?

PHILOMELE: Not me either. *(Indicates Ariadne:)* But she might.

MAIA: I'm not afraid of her. She'll follow her brother into the labyrinth and never come out. Won't you, Ariadne?

ARIADNE: I don't know what you're talking about.

MAIA: I'm talking about the labyrinth of Daedalus.

CAENEUS: *(Threatening:)* The giant maze. The one they've been building day and night for almost a year.

(As the dialogue continues, the children form a chain winding around Ariadne and The Minotaur and coming between them.)

IASON: The most fabulous prison ever imagined. An inescapable prison.

CAENEUS: And they're building it right here under the palace!

PHILOMELE: Soon the Athenian ship will come, with seven youths and seven maidens. The tribute they owe for the death of Prince Minos.

CAENEUS: For the murder of Prince Minos.

PHILOMELE: They say it was an accident.

CAENEUS: On their shores. Under the protection of their hospitality.

IASON: Now they'll pay. Fourteen times forever, they'll pay.

MAIA: And The Minotaur will pay. And Ariadne too if she isn't careful.

PHILOMELE: All the handsomest boys and the prettiest girls...

IASON: Every nine years, seven youths and seven maidens will sail from Athens to Crete. And they'll enter the maze —

CAENEUS: The labyrinth of Daedalus!

IASON: And they'll never come out.

CAENEUS: If this north wind keeps up, they could be here tonight.

(Ariadne is locked between the arms of a pair of children. She breaks away and faces her tormentors.)

ARIADNE: Yes, I know! Everyone knows. Athens must pay blood tribute to Crete — fourteen young men and women to be shut up in the labyrinth until they die. But what does that have to do with me? Or with Asterion.

MAIA: *(Indicating The Minotaur:)* Don't you know? The labyrinth will be his prison too.

ARIADNE: No! That's nonsense.

(The Minotaur snarls and lowers his head as if to charge. Ariadne speaks to him softly.)

It's ridiculous. She's making it up.

MAIA: There's to be a special chamber for him in the very center of the maze.

ARIADNE: *(To The Minotaur:)* Don't listen to her.

CAENEUS: There will be miles and miles of passages within passages...

PHILOMELE: More twists and turns than a tangle of thread...

MAIA: And the beauty of it is, no matter what path the Greek murderers take, it will lead them straight to the monster in the heart of the maze!

IASON: And then the Minotaur will devour them—

CAENEUS: And spit out their bones!

THE MINOTAUR: First, I'll devour you. I'll spit out your bones!

(Ariadne tries to come between Iason and her brother.)

ARIADNE: *(To The Minotaur:)* Ignore them. They're only trying to make you mad.

IASON: He'll gobble up every last Athenian. The boys first, and the girls for dessert. A fourteen-course feast.

ARIADNE: He's not a monster. He doesn't eat human flesh.

IASON: He'll eat it or starve.

MAIA: If he's hungry enough, he might eat you.

IASON: Unless you're a monster as well, too tough to chew.

CAENEUS: Let's see if you're a monster. Let's have a look at your horns.

(Caeneus advances on Ariadne.)

ARIADNE: I don't have horns!

IASON: *(Also advancing on Ariadne:)* Show us.

ARIADNE: *(Trying unsuccessfully to fend them off:)* Leave me alone! Stop it! Let go!

IASON: If you're really not a monster, then what have you got to be afraid of?

(The Minotaur bellows fearsomely and charges at Maia and Iason. They retreat to a safe distance but then stop and look for stones to throw. Most of the other children run away but one small child falls. The Minotaur advances and seems about to gore the child. Ariadne grabs hold of her brother's arm.)

ARIADNE: Asterion! No. Don't. Please!

(The Minotaur stops short of attacking the child, who gets up and runs away, along with Maia, Iason, and the rest of their compatriots. Phaedra remains on stage unseen by Ariadne and The Minotaur. They brush themselves off and catch their breath.)

THE MINOTAUR: Are you all right?

ARIADNE: Yes. Are you?

THE MINOTAUR: Yes. But...I had that dream again last night. About the labyrinth.

ARIADNE: Oh.

THE MINOTAUR: Even when I'm far up in the hills, inside a cave, I can hear them building it. Especially at night. When everything is quiet. I dreamed they were building it for me.

ARIADNE: It was only a dream.

THE MINOTAUR: But what if the things we know in dreams turn out to be true?

ARIADNE: Everything Maia was saying, she only says it to upset you. If you don't let it bother you, she'll leave you alone. *(Pause.)* The labyrinth is a prison for the Athenians. That's all.

THE MINOTAUR: How do you know that? How do you know it's not for me too?

ARIADNE: Because she's a liar. Everybody knows that. And because Father wouldn't do that. I know he wouldn't.

THE MINOTAUR: King Minos doesn't believe that he is my father.

ARIADNE: Yes, he does. Of course he does. After all, if he didn't believe you were his son, he would have exposed you at birth. He didn't kill you then, so why should he want to kill you now?

THE MINOTAUR: Because then it wasn't so obvious...

(Pause. He touches his horns.)

I know what people say, Ariadne. That Poseidon is punishing King Minos through me. That my real father is the spirit of the white bull. That's why I'm not welcome in the palace.

ARIADNE: Our mother loved our father. And he loved her.

THE MINOTAUR: Yes. And that's one more reason for him to hate me. Because I killed her.

ARIADNE: Don't say that!

THE MINOTAUR: But it's true.

ARIADNE: It was nobody's fault. Lots of women die in childbirth.

THE MINOTAUR: Maybe so. But he blames me anyway. *(Silence.)* In my dream...

ARIADNE: Yes?

THE MINOTAUR: In my dream, they are building the prison for me. And when they're done, the soldiers come for me. They come to throw me in the labyrinth. But every other time when I've had the dream you were there when the soldiers came, and you wouldn't let them take me—until last night. Last night, you weren't there.

ARIADNE: I would never let anybody hurt you, Asterion. You know that, don't you?

THE MINOTAUR: I know you love me, Ariadne. But what if there's nothing you can do to save me? *(Pause.)* Or what if it's too late?

ARIADNE: When I am queen, you will live in the palace with me. You'll have the best room in the palace, as many servants as you want to wait on you. You'll have the best ship in the harbor, whatever you want to eat and drink—

THE MINOTAUR: Let's run away.

ARIADNE: Run away?

THE MINOTAUR: Yes, now, before they come for me. Let's sail away. I'm tired of waiting for things to change.

ARIADNE: But this is our home.

THE MINOTAUR: No. It's your home.

(Pause.)

ARIADNE: Where would we go? If we ran away.

THE MINOTAUR: Anywhere. Anywhere we could be safe. Anywhere we could be together.

ARIADNE: *(Gently mocking:)* Sure. We'll sail away to a desert island and raise sheep. We'll be king and queen of the cattle.

THE MINOTAUR: Don't. Don't tease me.

ARIADNE: I'm sorry! I didn't mean it like that. Really. Nothing matters more to me than you do, Asterion.

THE MINOTAUR: Not even being queen?

ARIADNE: Not more. No. Of course not.

THE MINOTAUR: But it means a lot to you.

ARIADNE: Yes. Because when I'm queen, we can do what we want, we can live however we want to live. No one will be able to hurt us.

THE MINOTAUR: You won't be able to make them stop hating me.

ARIADNE: At least I can make them stop throwing stones at you.

THE MINOTAUR: Who says they won't do something much worse?

ARIADNE: I won't let them. Everything will be all right. Believe me. You just have to be patient — you have to learn to ignore what other people say. *(Pause.)* It's getting late. I should go.

THE MINOTAUR: Not yet.

ARIADNE: Yes. I should have been home already. If the Athenian tribute ship actually does arrive tonight...

THE MINOTAUR: Do you think it will?

ARIADNE: It could. If the wind keeps up.

THE MINOTAUR: And what if my dream turns out to be true? What if —

ARIADNE: Don't worry. Everything will be all right. I promise.

(They embrace and then each turns to go in a separate direction. The Minotaur hesitates and turns back to Ariadne.)

THE MINOTAUR: You'll come tomorrow, won't you?

ARIADNE: Yes. Like always.

(She gives him another hug.)

See you tomorrow!

(The Minotaur leaves. Ariadne watches him go and is about to leave too, when Phaedra appears.)

PHAEDRA: Ariadne!

ARIADNE: Phaedra! What are you doing here? Were you eavesdropping?

PHAEDRA: I was listening. You should spend more time listening. Instead of playing games in the woods and hiding in caves. You would learn things. Things the heir to the throne of Crete should know.

ARIADNE: Like what?

PHAEDRA: Like what people say about you, for instance.

ARIADNE: I don't care what they say about me.

PHAEDRA: They say you are bringing shame to the kingdom by running around like a wild animal, keeping company with monsters.

ARIADNE: Why should I care? It doesn't matter what they think.

PHAEDRA: Doesn't it even matter what they think about him? About The Minotaur?

ARIADNE: He has a name.

PHAEDRA: In the Athenian court, he is known as "The terrible Minotaur of Crete." A monster who must be fed on human flesh. Which is why they believe they must send their young men and women to be sacrificed. Or else King Minos will have the fearsome beast brought to Athens to be set loose. Better to deliver just fourteen youths and maidens to their death each year than for the monster to ravage the entire country.

ARIADNE: But that makes no sense. As soon as they get here, as soon as they see him, they'll know he's not what they've been told. And then —

PHAEDRA: No one will ever return to Athens to tell what they've seen. So it won't matter whether he's actually what they believe him to be or not.

ARIADNE: But why do they believe it?

PHAEDRA: Because it's what Father wants them to believe. He wants to lure the finest young men of Athens to their death. You don't think they'd come just to walk through a maze, do you? Where would be the excitement in that? But to slay the famous monster? They'll be standing in line to prove their courage. Maybe even Theseus will come. That's what Father is hoping for. Since Prince Minos died in Athens, it seems only fair that King Aegeus should send his son and heir to die in Crete.

ARIADNE: But what if Theseus kills Asterion?

PHAEDRA: What if he does? Theseus will never escape from the labyrinth. No one will ever escape.

(Philomele enters. She hurries towards Phaedra and Ariadne.)

ARIADNE: I have to go warn him.

PHAEDRA: *(Indicating Philomele:)* Shh. Not now.

ARIADNE: I promised him I would keep him safe.

PHILOMELE: Phaedra! Ariadne! Everybody is looking for you. The sails of the Athenian ship have been sighted. You have to come back to the palace and get ready for the banquet tonight. The boar is on the spit, and the goats have been slaughtered and skinned.

PHAEDRA: We were just coming.

(Phaedra reaches to take Ariadne's hand. Ariadne hesitates, looking off in the direction taken by The Minotaur.)

PHILOMELE: *(Taking Phaedra's other hand:)* Come on.

PHAEDRA: *(Whispering to Ariadne:)* You can slip out later. During the banquet.

ARIADNE: But—

PHAEDRA: If you try to go to him now, they'll just come looking for you, and then they'll find him too.

(Philomele pulls on Phaedra's hand and leads her off stage. Reluctantly, Ariadne follows. As they exit, The Chorus enters and continues to construct the labyrinth. The pace of the construction is intense, but controlled and deliberate, not frenetic.)

CHORUS: Set it in stone.
Confusion and conflict.
No one will ever enter and leave.
Blood of them all
will flow like a river
and Athens will mourn
her youths and her maidens.
The offspring of shame,
no one will mourn him.
Set it in stone.
Confusion and conflict.

(The Chorus completes the construction of the labyrinth and separates into two groups—MINOANS and ATHENIANS. One of the Athenians is THESEUS. After everyone else is

assembled, the KING of Crete enters, flanked by SOLDIERS and accompanied by Ariadne and Phaedra.)

MINOANS: We grant you honor, youths and maidens
who have come from a distant shore.
Handsome youths and pretty maidens
who come to meet the Minotaur.

ATHENIANS: We have heard he breathes out fire.
We have heard he drinks hot blood.
Will he swallow us entire,
or chew us as his cud?

MINOANS: Handsome youths and pretty maidens,
welcome to the Isle of Crete.
We humbly pray the Lord Poseidon,
may your stay be long and sweet.

ATHENIAN GIRLS: Some say his horns are tipped with gold,
some say with poison.

ATHENIAN BOYS: Some say he toys with the girls and then
he gores them.

FIRST ATHENIAN: I thought I would live to climb Mount Pelion.

SECOND ATHENIAN: I thought I would live to wear my wedding gown.

THIRD ATHENIAN: I want to learn to dance and play the lyre.

FOURTH ATHENIAN: I want to laugh with my friends beside the fire.

FIFTH ATHENIAN: I want to live 'til I grow old.

MINOANS: Handsome youths and pretty maidens,
we bid you welcome to our shore.

Is there one among you children
who dares to face the Minotaur?

(Theseus steps forward.)

THESEUS: I do.

KING: You want to fight The Minotaur?

THESEUS: Yes.

KING: Then you must be very eager to meet your death. Who are you?

THESEUS: I am Theseus, son of King Aegeus, your majesty.

KING: Aegeus is a fool to be so careless of his son's life. His only son. Or perhaps you are an imposter?

THESEUS: My father sent this token with me, so you would know I come here with his blessing and as the true heir to the throne of Athens.

(Theseus is wearing a signet ring which he now removes and holds out. A soldier takes the ring from Theseus and hands it to the King, who examines it.)

KING: True son or no, Aegeus will never again see you alive.

THESEUS: I give myself into the keeping of the gods. If I earn their favor, they will send home a son worthy of a noble father.

KING: The gods do not favor the sons of murderers!

(Angrily, the King throws the ring to the ground. It rolls near to Phaedra, who first looks to see if anyone is watching and then quickly picks it up.)

THESEUS: My father is no murderer.

KING: Tell that to the beast inside the maze! Tomorrow at dawn, Theseus, you shall enter the labyrinth. Alone. If you do not reappear by sunset — with the head of The Minotaur — then your companions will follow you into the maze.

THESEUS: And what if I emerge victorious? What then?

KING: Name the prize and you shall have it. Gold? Ships? My daughter's hand in marriage?

THESEUS: Freedom. I want freedom for Athens from Minoan rule. And from all our debts to Crete.

KING: Freedom?! For that tribe of ungrateful savages? They wouldn't know what to do with it.

THESEUS: I also want provisions for the journey home and safe passage through your waters for myself and my shipmates.

KING: Very well then. But it's a lucky thing for Athens that her people need not live in fear of your success.

(All exit, except for Ariadne. As soon as the others are out of sight, she begins looking for her brother. She calls to him urgently, but quietly.)

ARIADNE: Asterion? Are you there? I have to talk to you.

(Cautiously, The Minotaur emerges into the open.)

THE MINOTAUR: Are you alone?

ARIADNE: Yes.

(He runs to her and they embrace.)

The Athenians are here.

THE MINOTAUR: Yes, I know. I saw their ship in the harbor. The ship with black sails. *(Pause.)* It's true, isn't it? Everything they said? About the labyrinth. About me. I am to be the monster inside the maze?

ARIADNE: Not if you get away now, while everyone is still at the banquet. But you have to hurry.

THE MINOTAUR: What about you? You'll come with me, won't you?

(Pause.)

ARIADNE: I want to, but...

THE MINOTAUR: But you won't. Because you also want to stay here and become queen some day.

ARIADNE: If I came with you, it would only make it more dangerous for you.

THE MINOTAUR: I don't want to be alone.

ARIADNE: You won't be. Not forever. One day it will be safe for you to come back. One day I'll send word. Wherever you are, I'll find you. And you'll come home. *(Pause.)* But for now, you have to leave. Go down to the harbor, steal a boat. You can be a mile away before anyone knows you're gone. And I have to go back to the banquet, or else they'll come looking for me, and then —

THE MINOTAUR: I won't leave without you.

ARIADNE: But you have to! You have to go now.

THE MINOTAUR: No.

ARIADNE: Did you know that Theseus is here? He wants to slay the famous Minotaur. He wants to prove that he really is the long-lost son of Aegeus.

THE MINOTAUR: Theseus? *(Mocking:)* The great Athenian hero has come to Crete to fight me?

ARIADNE: Yes! He's been killing bandits and ogres all up and down the coast of Greece.

THE MINOTAUR: And now he wants to kill me?

ARIADNE: Yes, so you see —

THE MINOTAUR: Let him try.

ARIADNE: What?

THE MINOTAUR: I'll be happy to fight him. To do battle with Theseus.

ARIADNE: But he'll kill you.

THE MINOTAUR: Maybe. Maybe not. Maybe I'll kill him. That would please Father, wouldn't it? If I were to kill the son of Aegeus?

ARIADNE: Yes, it probably would. It probably would make him very happy, but it wouldn't do you any good because —

(Ariadne stops mid-sentence. She hears — and so does the audience — the sound of soldiers approaching.)

Listen... They're coming for you. Hurry!

THE MINOTAUR: No. I'm tired of running away.

ARIADNE: Don't be stupid.

(First one SOLDIER, and then ANOTHER, enters the stage. The first soldier sees Asterion and points to him.)

FIRST SOLDIER: There he is!

ARIADNE: Come on! I'll go with you. Now! Please.

(Ariadne takes her brother's hand and tries to pull him along with her.)

THE MINOTAUR: Run if you want to. I'm staying here to fight Theseus.

(The rest of the SOLDIERS swarm onto the stage and surround The Minotaur. Ariadne tries to stay by his side but the soldiers

shove her out of the way. She watches helplessly as they exit with Asterion in tow, and remains standing alone center stage. Lights fade to black.)

(The Chorus enters and forms the labyrinth; they take center stage, pushing Ariadne aside. The lights begin to rise faintly – it is just before dawn – and continue to rise as the scene progresses. Mournful sounds emanate from within the labyrinth. They might be moans, or growls, or Asterion calling Ariadne's name, or simply the wind. Ariadne approaches the entrance to the labyrinth. Stops. Listens. Steps back. Phaedra enters and sees Ariadne.)

PHAEDRA: Ariadne!

ARIADNE: Phaedra! What are you doing here?

PHAEDRA: Looking for you. What do you think? I came to warn you, about the soldiers –

ARIADNE: They've already come.

PHAEDRA: Were you in time to warn Asterion?

ARIADNE: He refused to run away. As soon as he heard that Theseus had come to Crete to fight him –

PHAEDRA: Theseus will kill him!

ARIADNE: I know. I told him that. But –

PHAEDRA: Not that it will make any difference. So what if Theseus slays the monster? He won't be able to get out of the labyrinth. He'll wander forever until he dies of thirst and hunger.

ARIADNE: Phaedra! The "monster" is your brother!

PHAEDRA: I know!

ARIADNE: Then why are you fretting about Theseus?

PHAEDRA: I'm not.

ARIADNE: It sounded like you were. *(Pause.)* I saw you pick up his ring.

PHAEDRA: So?

ARIADNE: You care more about that stranger than you do about your own brother!

PHAEDRA: The ring was lying on the ground at my feet. So I picked it up. It doesn't mean anything... But at least if his head is cut off, Asterion will die quickly. Can you imagine wandering alone in the dark until...I mean, even though Theseus is our enemy, you have to admit it takes courage...

ARIADNE: To walk into the labyrinth? It takes stupidity. That's all. It's a trap.

PHAEDRA: But he doesn't know it's a trap. He thinks he's going to face a dangerous beast and that if he kills it, he saves his country.

ARIADNE: He should know that the king of Crete would never give him a fighting chance.

PHAEDRA: How? How should he know that?

(Pause.)

ARIADNE: Maybe we should tell him.

PHAEDRA: What?

ARIADNE: Maybe we should tell him that it's a trap. Because you're right. How is he supposed to know if we don't tell him?

PHAEDRA: You want to sneak into the Athenian camp and talk to Theseus?

ARIADNE: Why not? *(Pause.)* Don't look at me like that. You're the one who's been singing his praises.

PHAEDRA: Maybe I do feel a little bit sorry for him, but I'm not a traitor!

ARIADNE: I'm not talking about treason!

PHAEDRA: Helping our enemy? That's treason. *(Looking around furtively:)* We'd better go back to the palace. It's past daybreak. If anybody finds us here it won't matter whose daughters we are...

ARIADNE: Theseus is going to kill Asterion. For no reason. And then he's going to die too. For no reason. And you want to just let that happen?

(Pause.)

PHAEDRA: Even if you did warn Theseus, what good would it do? He can't simply turn around and go back to Athens. He has to enter the maze. He has to face The Minotaur.

ARIADNE: But does he have to kill him? Suppose there was some way for him to escape, and Asterion too...

PHAEDRA: But there's not. The labyrinth is inescapable. So let's go.

(Phaedra starts walking away, almost dragging Ariadne along with her. Ariadne, looking back over her shoulder at the labyrinth, doesn't see where she is going and stumbles, catching her skirt on a rock or a bramble. She tries to pull herself loose and her hem begins to unravel. In order to free her skirt, Ariadne must follow the loose thread back to the place where it is caught. Phaedra waits for her impatiently. Suddenly Ariadne stops and catches her breath.)

ARIADNE: Oh!

PHAEDRA: What is it?

ARIADNE: *(Excitedly, looking from the thread in her hand to the* *entrance of the labyrinth:)* A thread! If you could follow it...if you unwound a thread —

(Ariadne glances at Phaedra and cuts herself off abruptly.)

PHAEDRA: What?

ARIADNE: Oh, nothing. A loose thread, that's all. Help me untangle it.

(As they work together to untangle the thread, Ariadne is agitated and struggles to hide her excitement.)

PHAEDRA: Hold still. You're making it worse.

ARIADNE: Can't you hurry up?

PHAEDRA: I'm trying. There. You're untangled. Let's go.

(Ariadne and Phaedra exit together, nearly running. The Chorus remains onstage representing the labyrinth, which grows increasingly animated as the moans and growls from within its heart increase.)

CHORUS: Set it in stone.
Confusion and conflict.
The monster awaits,
never to leave.
Where is the hero
who will enter the labyrinth?
Where is the young man
whose father will grieve?

(It is now daylight. Theseus enters, his sword drawn. He approaches the labyrinth, which reaches out, ready to pull him in. Just as he begins to enter, Ariadne appears. She is wearing a cloak which obscures much of her face and body.)

ARIADNE: No! Theseus! Wait!

(He spins around to face her.)

Don't go in. You'll be lost.

THESEUS: Who are you? What do you want?

ARIADNE: I want to help you.

(Theseus moves closer to Ariadne. He tries to get a better look at her, but she draws the cloak more closely around her.)

THESEUS: Are you a goddess?

ARIADNE: No, just a girl.

THESEUS: Then how can you help me?

ARIADNE: I can tell you how to escape from the maze.

THESEUS: Can you tell me how to kill the monster?

ARIADNE: There is no monster.

THESEUS: *(Laughing in disbelief:)* No hideous creature nursed on human blood? Half-man, half-bull?

ARIADNE: It's only a story, told to lure would-be heroes to their death.

THESEUS: There is no Minotaur? He doesn't exist?

ARIADNE: He...he's not a monster. He has the horns of a bull. But he's a boy all the same. A young man. Like you.

THESEUS: How long are his horns? How sharp?

ARIADNE: His name is Asterion.

THESEUS: I don't need to know his name in order to kill him.

ARIADNE: You don't need to kill him.

THESEUS: No? I suppose I should let him eat me. And eat my companions?

ARIADNE: He won't eat you! That's what I'm trying to tell you. You don't need to be afraid of him.

THESEUS: But the human sacrifice? Every nine years for all of eternity, fourteen young men and women...?

ARIADNE: It's not Asterion who requires the sacrifice. It's the king. He has commanded Daedalus to build the most elaborate maze the world has ever known, an inescapable prison without locks or keys. The Minotaur is only the bait — laid to ensnare you. *(Pause.)* Your death will make King Minos very happy.

THESEUS: An inescapable prison? But you can tell me how to escape it?

ARIADNE: Yes.

THESEUS: *(Suspiciously:)* How do you know all this? Who are you?

(Theseus pushes Ariadne's cloak aside to reveal her face. He studies her.)

I saw you at the banquet last night. You're the princess Ariadne, the oldest daughter of King Minos.

ARIADNE: Yes.

THESEUS: Then why are you here offering to help the son of your father's enemy?

ARIADNE: Because Asterion is my brother. I want you to help me save his life.

THESEUS: *(Recoiling:)* You want me to save the life of The Minotaur?

ARIADNE: Yes. And your own as well.

(She withdraws a ball of thread from inside her cloak.)

I will show you how to escape from the maze, if you promise to bring Asterion out along with you, unhurt. If you bring him back to Athens with you, then one day I will be queen and I'll —

THESEUS: But that's why I came here — to kill The Minotaur. Or, if The Minotaur kills me, then at least I've died a hero's death.

ARIADNE: It's not a very heroic way to die, wandering around lost in the dark until you starve to death.

THESEUS: Better to starve than bring home a monster to ravage the countryside.

ARIADNE: He's not a monster!

THESEUS: So you keep telling me. But I'm not a fool. Tell your father that I can't be deceived by pretty girls telling lies.

(Theseus strides towards the labyrinth, his sword in hand. Ariadne runs after him and grabs his arm. He tries to shake her off. Note that each time Theseus and/or Ariadne approaches the labyrinth, it seems to come alive, reaching out to pull them in, the whispers and moans from within becoming louder.)

ARIADNE: Stop! Please!

THESEUS: Let me go. I don't want to hurt you.

ARIADNE: No! Listen — ouch!

(In the struggle, Ariadne has been nicked by Theseus' sword. She yelps in pain. He quickly sheathes his sword.)

THESEUS: I'm sorry.

ARIADNE: It's just a scratch.

THESEUS: But you're bleeding. Let me —

ARIADNE: I'm all right.

(Theseus tears a strip off his tunic and ties it around Ariadne's arm.)

THESEUS: Does that help?

ARIADNE: Thank you. Yes.

THESEUS: I didn't mean to hurt you, but—

ARIADNE: But you think my father sent me to trick you into letting your guard down?

THESEUS: What else am I supposed to think?

ARIADNE: That I'm telling you the truth.

THESEUS: Even if I did believe you, what difference would it make? If I want to save my own life and my friends' lives, I must emerge from the labyrinth by sundown with the head of The Minotaur.

ARIADNE: With his head, yes, but who says it has to be severed from his body? Think of it. You'll be able to say you tamed the famous Minotaur. Imagine the glory. Lots of heroes kill monsters.

THESEUS: And how am I supposed to tame this savage beast? Is he going to put his tail between his legs and follow me like a lost lamb?

ARIADNE: Asterion is not—

THESEUS: Yes, I know. You keep telling me, he's not a monster.

ARIADNE: But you don't believe me.

THESEUS: *(Sincerely:)* Can you give me a reason why I should trust you?

ARIADNE: What if I went with you? Into the labyrinth.

THESEUS: You would do that? You're not afraid?

ARIADNE: No more afraid than you are.

(Pause.)

THESEUS: You said you could show me how to find my way out of the maze?

(Smiling, Ariadne holds up the ball of thread. She steps some distance away and tosses it to Theseus, keeping hold of the loose end. He catches it and she follows the thread to him. He looks at her with amazement and delight.)

ARIADNE: You promise you will keep him safe in Athens with you, until I become queen? Then I will send for him.

THESEUS: Yes. *(Pause.)* When I am king of Athens and you are queen of Crete, must we be enemies as our fathers and grandfathers have been?

ARIADNE: I don't know.

(Side by side, Ariadne and Theseus walk towards the labyrinth. At the entrance, Ariadne pauses and ties the loose end of thread to the "gate." As they enter the labyrinth, Theseus draws his sword. Ariadne stops short. She puts her hand on his sword hand.)

If he sees your sword, it will scare him. He'll think you're coming to kill him.

(Theseus hesitates a moment and then sheathes his sword.)

THESEUS: I'll leave it sheathed.

ARIADNE: But why bring it at all?

THESEUS: In case he attacks us.

ARIADNE: He won't. He would only attack if he were threatened.

THESEUS: Then there's nothing to worry about. I promise I won't draw my sword unless we're in danger.

(Without waiting to listen to any more arguments, Theseus leads the way into the labyrinth. The labyrinth opens up to fill the stage and entangle Theseus and Ariadne. It harries them and tosses them about as they make their way into the depths of the maze. Ariadne follows behind Theseus, unwinding the ball of thread as she goes. Members of the Chorus whisper to them as they pass and echo bits and pieces of their words so that all conversation is distorted, almost impossible to carry on. The murmur of the Chorus is virtually constant, overlapping all the other dialogue unless indicated.)

Ariadne? Are you still here?

CHORUS: here here here

ARIADNE: I'm right here.

(Ariadne and Theseus strive to stick close together, but the Chorus works actively to separate them.)

CHORUS: here here

ARIADNE: Asterion? Where are you?

CHORUS: where where you you you you you

ARIADNE: Don't be afraid. It's me, Ariadne. We've come to help you.

CHORUS: afraid fraid frayed Ariadne adne you you

ARIADNE: Theseus won't hurt you.

CHORUS: theseus ssuss ssuss susss   hurt hurt hurt you

THESEUS: I won't hurt you.

CHORUS: hurt hurt hurt hurt you you you

(The Chorus now opens up a space to reveal The Minotaur, crouching like an animal. Ariadne stumbles into the space, followed a moment later by Theseus. When Asterion sees his

sister, he straightens up and starts towards her eagerly. Then he catches sight of Theseus standing just behind her. He freezes.)

ARIADNE: No one will hurt you. I promise. Asterion —

CHORUS: hurt hurt hurt hurt you you promise misssss ssisss ssissss

(The Chorus continues to hiss and murmur, drowning out anything Ariadne tries to say. She moves a step or two closer to The Minotaur. He backs away. Theseus moves with Ariadne, staying close to her. He puts a hand protectively on her arm or shoulder. The Minotaur drops down again to all fours, paws the ground, and tosses his head. Growling, The Minotaur advances towards Ariadne and Theseus. Theseus draws his sword and steps forward.)

ARIADNE: Theseus! Don't!

(Ariadne tries to hold Theseus back, but he shakes her off. Some members of the Chorus continue to hiss and murmur while others begin to chant.)

CHORUS: Here is the monster.
Where is the hero?

(Gradually the whole Chorus joins the chant. The murmur of their words builds and fades in a regular, inexorable rhythm, like ocean waves. As they chant, the members of the Chorus divide into two groups; half stand by Theseus, half by The Minotaur. The hero and the monster size each other up. Then slowly, warily, menacingly, they approach one another. At first, the Chorus mirrors their actions but gradually it takes over, manipulating the combatants, guiding them through a slow-motion, stylized fight. Ariadne tries to break in between them but is blocked by the Chorus. The chant continues, mounting to a painful intensity — not loud, but overwhelming, like the roar of blood in one's ears. As the fight approaches its climax, the Chorus closes in around Theseus and The Minotaur, obscuring

them from the audience's view and leaving Ariadne on the outside looking in. Ariadne screams. Silence. The Chorus parts to reveal that Theseus has beheaded The Minotaur.)

ARIADNE: What have you done?

THESEUS: I defended myself—and you—against his attack. That's all.

(A sob catches in Ariadne's throat. She tries to restrain it. Theseus goes to her and reaches out a hand to touch her. She pulls away from him.)

ARIADNE: Don't touch me.

THESEUS: I'm sorry.

(Pause. Theseus cleans and sheathes his sword. He picks up the head of The Minotaur and puts it in a bag that hangs from his sword belt.)

ARIADNE: *(Horrified:)* What are you doing?

THESEUS: If I don't take his head, then it's all for nothing.

ARIADNE: I promised I would never let anyone hurt him. And then I led you right to him.

THESEUS: He would have killed me. He might have killed you too.

ARIADNE: No!

(Ariadne sits on the ground next to her brother's body and begins to cry. Theseus hesitates and then puts a hand gently on her shoulder.)

THESEUS: Ariadne—

ARIADNE: Leave me alone!

THESEUS: It's time to go.

ARIADNE: Then go! You don't need me.

(She thrusts the ball of yarn into his hands.)

I should have run away with him when there was still time.

THESEUS: If they find you here, they will know you showed me the way. They'll kill you for a traitor.

ARIADNE: I don't care.

THESEUS: Ariadne, please...I can't let you die here. What good would it do anyone?

(In a daze, Ariadne allows Theseus to draw her to her feet.)

THESEUS: We'll go together to the entrance. You can slip out before me while no one is watching. Then you should go back to the palace. Later, when the court is assembled, I'll come out alone. No one will ever know you even spoke to me.

(Winding the thread as he goes, Theseus leads Ariadne back the way they have come. She follows numbly. They exit. The Chorus remains onstage, closing around the body of The Minotaur.)

CHORUS: The offspring of shame,
no one will mourn him.
Set it in stone,
confusion and conflict.

(Members of the Chorus break off from the labyrinth to become the children of the court; they include Philomele, Maia, Iason, and Phaedra. Phaedra is subdued and anxious, but the others are buzzing with excitement. It is now late afternoon.)

PHILOMELE: I don't see the point of waiting around here. Nothing is going to happen until sunset.

CAENEUS: Everybody else is here.

(While the others are talking, Phaedra draws near to the labyrinth, looking around suspiciously. She spies the loose,

tangled skein that was a ball of thread hidden in a corner and picks it up.)

IASON: You just want to see how loud those Athenian girls are going to scream when they get shoved into the labyrinth.

CAENEUS: Sure. Don't you?

IASON: I wonder if The Minotaur will spit out their bones and hair and clothes. Or will he eat every last bit of them?

PHILOMELE: Maybe he's dead already. Maybe Theseus killed him.

IASON: That Athenian show-off? He couldn't skewer a roasted pig.

CAENEUS: Why don't you go in and find out? See who got skewered.

(Caeneus gives Iason a shove.)

MAIA: Philomele will go with you — to keep you from being lonely. Won't you, Philomele?

(Caeneus and Maia shove Iason and Philomele towards the labyrinth.)

CAENEUS: Come back and give us a full report. If you can find your way out.

MAIA: I'll bet it's nice and cozy in there.

PHAEDRA: Leave them alone. They didn't do anything to you.

CAENEUS: I'm just having fun. They can take a joke. *(To Iason and Philomele:)* Can't you?

IASON: Sure.

(Philomele shrugs. Phaedra approaches her and offers a consoling gesture.)

MAIA: *(To Phaedra:)* What's the matter with you? You've been acting strange all day.

IASON: *(Derisively:)* She's probably been shedding tears over the fate of those poor Athenians.

MAIA: Or maybe over the fate of one particular Athenian? A particularly handsome Athenian?

IASON: *(To Phaedra:)* I saw you leaving the banquet last night. Where did you go?

MAIA: Were you skulking around the Athenian camp? Did you have a tryst with Theseus?

PHAEDRA: No! Of course not!

CAENEUS: Don't worry, Phaedra. They're only teasing. We all know there's no such thing as a handsome Athenian.

PHILOMELE: Hush. They're coming.

(King Minos enters with his entourage; Ariadne is among the group. When all are formally assembled near the entrance to the labyrinth, the king addresses the leader of his soldiers.)

KING: Bring the Athenians here. It's time for them to follow their leader into the maze.

(A contingent of soldiers is about to leave, but they stop as they see Theseus emerge from the labyrinth. He holds up the head of The Minotaur and approaches the king.)

THESEUS: Your majesty, I have slain The Minotaur.

(The crowd murmurs in amazement.)

KING: *(Addressing the crowd:)* Silence! *(To Theseus:)* I can see that you've killed the monster. And that you've escaped from the labyrinth. Daedalus is the greatest artificer the world has ever known. He swore to me that no one would ever find his way out of the prison he designed. And yet you have.

THESEUS: I have fulfilled your conditions, and now I claim the prize: provisions for the journey, safe passage through your waters, and freedom for my country.

KING: How did you do it?

THESEUS: I am well-known, your majesty, for my victories in battle.

KING: But you are not well-known, I think, for your prowess in solving puzzles.

THESEUS: An ordinary man may do great things when the gods are on his side.

KING: Or when a traitor assists him.

(Pause. King Minos holds up the signet ring.)

Is this your ring?

THESEUS: *(Startled:)* Yes. No. I mean, it is my father's...

KING: And you gave it to my daughter.

THESEUS: No! Never!

KING: Then how did it come to be under her pillow?

(A stunned silence meets this revelation. Theseus studiously avoids glancing at Ariadne. She has been watching the proceedings with stony impassivity and continues to do so.)

THESEUS: I have no idea, your majesty. I gave the ring to you, and —

KING: Does it have powers to bewitch? Or is it just the same old story — a handsome stranger, a pretty girl...

THESEUS: I gave the ring to you. You threw it on the ground. I'm not the kind of coward who would lure a girl to betray her —

KING: Phaedra! Come here!

THESEUS: Phae-!?

(Theseus suppresses his gasp of surprise and glances involuntarily at Ariadne. Shocked into responsiveness, she meets his gaze for a moment. All other eyes are on Phaedra, who approaches her father and kneels before him, frightened and trembling. Nervously, she plays with the skein of thread.)

KING: Did Theseus give you this ring?

PHAEDRA: No! You know I would never —

KING: Then where did you get it?

PHAEDRA: It was lying on the ground — where you threw it. I picked it up, that's all. I didn't mean any harm by it.

KING: What is that?

(He points to the tangle of thread.)

PHAEDRA: Nothing. A ball of thread.

KING: Give it to me!

(Phaedra hands the king the skein of thread, and he examines it thoughtfully.)

PHAEDRA: I found it. Over there. By the labyrinth.

KING: *(A dawning realization:)* You plotted with him. You conspired to lead him out of —

PHAEDRA: No! I didn't do anything.

THESEUS: She's telling you the truth. I've never spoken to her, never given anything to her. I never saw her except last night when you and all the court were there. Until now.

KING: Someone helped you. I'm sure of it.

PHAEDRA: Not me. I wouldn't.

KING: Then who?

PHAEDRA: No one. I don't know.

(*The King draws his sword. Theseus steps between the King and Phaedra.*)

THESEUS: I claim safe passage home as you have promised.

KING: And I'll keep my promise — as soon as you tell me who the traitor is.

(*Silence. The King raises his sword and is about to bring it down on the neck of Theseus when Ariadne steps forward.*)

ARIADNE: It was me. I helped him.

(*He stares at her for a long moment, then lets his sword drop to his side.*)

KING: I am cursed with monsters for children.

PHAEDRA: Father!

KING: Athenian, go home! Go home to your father. Whom the gods have blessed with a loyal son. As for these daughters, the palace of Minos will crumble into the sea before they take my place.

ARIADNE: Father, please. Phaedra didn't know anything about it. She would have stopped me if she'd known.

KING: But you, Ariadne? You led the son of my enemy out of the maze? (*Holds up the skein of thread:*) With this?

ARIADNE: Yes.

KING: *(Tossing the ball of thread to the ground:)* Theseus, take this traitor with you to Athens—or throw her into the sea. I don't want her on Minoan soil, alive or dead.

(The King turns sharply and exits, followed by his soldiers. After a moment's hesitation, Phaedra also follows with a sad, grateful backwards glance at Ariadne. Ariadne and Theseus are now alone on stage. He approaches her; she glances at The Minotaur's head, which he still holds, and turns away, shuddering.)

THESEUS: If you hadn't told your father that you helped me, you would still be safe, you would still be heir to the throne.

ARIADNE: You were going to let him kill you.

THESEUS: I'm sorry you've lost your kingdom—and your home. For my sake.

(In the distance we hear the Athenians approaching, laughing, shouting, singing. Theseus and Ariadne look in the direction of the sound.)

You'll come with me, won't you, Ariadne? You'll come with me to Athens?

ARIADNE: What would you say to your shipmates? And to your father, when you got home?

THESEUS: That you saved my life, twice. That Athens owes her freedom to you.

(Ariadne forces herself to look at The Minotaur's head. She reaches towards it. Theseus removes his cloak and tenderly wraps it around the head, then hands it to Ariadne who cradles it in her arms. The Athenians enter and hurry towards Theseus.)

When my father dies he will leave behind a strong country and under my rule it will become even stronger...I'll build an empire even greater than Crete's...thanks to you. *(Pause.)* Ariadne, I want you to be my queen. Will you?

ARIADNE: Queen of Athens?

(The Athenians surround Theseus, shouting joyfully, "The Minotaur is dead," "Long live Theseus," "Athens is free" etc. They sweep him away from Ariadne, leaving her alone. She watches for awhile and then turns away. At the height of the celebration, Theseus observes Ariadne walking towards the labyrinth. He breaks away from his companions.)

THESEUS: Stop! Ariadne! Wait! Where are you going?

ARIADNE: I want to bury him. I need to say goodbye.

(She picks up the skein of thread from the ground and begins to untangle it.)

THESEUS: We don't have much time.

(Ariadne hesitates for a moment, and then speaks decisively.)

ARIADNE: I'll meet you at the harbor. Go.

(She turns again to leave. He reaches out to her.)

THESEUS: We have to be ready to leave before the tide turns — or before your father changes his mind.

ARIADNE: I'll be there soon.

THESEUS: Wait 'til you see Athens, Ariadne. It's beautiful. You'll be happy there. You'll forget all about this — Crete and the labyrinth, it will be like a bad dream.

ARIADNE: I'm not going to Athens with you.

THESEUS: But —

ARIADNE: I can't stay here. I know that. So I'll be grateful if you will take me as far as Thera, or Naxos—anywhere that owes no allegiance to Athens or to Crete.

THESEUS: *(Incredulously:)* You want me to just drop you off on some rock in the middle of the sea? Even if you don't believe that you could ever come to love me—

ARIADNE: That's not the reason.

THESEUS: Then why?

ARIADNE: I won't be queen of an empire bought with my brother's blood.

(The rejoicing of the Athenians, which has continued in the background of this exchange, begins to settle down. Two of his shipmates now approach Theseus. He turns to them.)

FIRST ATHENIAN: Theseus, it's getting late...

THESEUS: *(Irritably:)* All right. I'll be there.

(Theseus gestures to his friends to leave him alone.)

SECOND ATHENIAN: Don't be too long about it.

(They rejoin the others who are, by now, all watching Theseus and Ariadne from a distance and whispering together.)

THESEUS: Ariadne, I can't just abandon you on some island somewhere. What would you do? Herd sheep? Tend cattle?

ARIADNE: Something like that.

THESEUS: Won't you even consider—

(She shakes her head. The other Athenians are now calling for Theseus to join them.)

Let me come with you into the labyrinth. Let me help you to bury him. That much at least I owe—

ARIADNE: Go on. Your shipmates are calling you.

THESEUS: I'll tell them to wait.

ARIADNE: No. They need you. *(Pause.)* Don't worry, I won't be lost.

(She shows him that she is holding the ball of thread.)

THESEUS: We won't leave without you.

ARIADNE: I know you won't.

(Reluctantly, Theseus parts from Ariadne and joins the other Athenians – who then merge into the labyrinth. As Ariadne enters, the "walls" part to make a clear path for her.)

CHORUS: Set it in stone.
Confusion and conflict.
No one will ever enter and leave.
Blood of them all
will flow like a river
and Athens will mourn
her youths and her maidens.

(The members of the Chorus guide Ariadne towards the heart of the maze, where her brother's body lies.)

The offspring of shame,
no one will mourn him.
So set it in stone.
Confusion and conflict.

(Ariadne kneels beside the body of her brother; in her arms is The Minotaur's head, still wrapped in Theseus' cloak. The Chorus forms a semi-circle behind her, facing the audience.)

CHORUS: Blood of them all
still flows like a river.
Shall we all mourn

our youths and our maidens?
The offspring of shame,
will anyone mourn him?
Will you set it in stone?
Confusion and conflict.

> *(Lovingly, Ariadne unwraps the head and sets it down. Then she covers her brother's body with Theseus' cloak. She remains kneeling by his side for a moment, then rises and walks off stage. The Chorus remains facing the audience.)*

Will you set it in stone,
confusion and conflict?

> *(The End.)*

The Author Speaks

What inspired you to write this play?

I had previously written a play called *Persephone Underground* which premiered at the Young People's Theatre of Ann Arbor, Michigan, in a lovely production directed by Kate Mendeloff. I was eager to work with Kate again and with the talented children and teens in YPT, so I began casting about for another story that would appeal to young performers ages 8-18 and to audiences of all ages. In *Persephone*, there is an allusion to the mythological hero Theseus, who slew The Minotaur, and his adventures seemed to catch the attention of the students in the cast. I began thinking about this tale, which involves romance, sibling rivalry, and conflicts of loyalty. In particular, I became interested in how the events might have looked from the Minotaur's point of view.

Have you dealt with the same theme in other works that you have written?

In *Medusa's Tale*, I also portrayed "heroes" and "monsters," complicating the relationships and motivations of these archetypal characters. Medusa and The Minotaur are both well-known for having been slain by famous heroes (namely Perseus and Theseus). I wanted to explore how they became monsters and what the world looked like from their perspective. I also wanted to explore the heroes' lives beyond the single moment of swinging a sword to cut off a head.

What do you hope to achieve with this work?

I hope to make the audience think about how it happens that complex human beings become cast in stereotypical roles, be it as heroes or monsters or ingénues, and to consider how young people might disrupt this process—how they might choose to shape their own lives instead of being molded by the pressure to conform.

What inspired you to become a playwright?
As a child, my favorite way to spend my time was to make up stories and act them out with my friends. Now, I make up stories and act them out in my head as I am writing them — and then I get to see actors, directors, and designers bring them to life. The joy of this process is what inspires me.

How did you research the subject?
Ovid's *Metamorphosis* was my primary source for the myth, but I read other versions as well and also looked at depictions of Theseus and the Minotaur in art.

Shakespeare gave advice to the players in *Hamlet*; if you could give advice to your cast what would it be?
Take your time. Think about what's happening. Speak clearly. Let the rhythm of the words carry you where you need to go. And pay attention to the punctuation!

About the Author

Carol S. Lashof is a playwright, librettist, and educator. Her plays have been produced by the Magic Theatre of San Francisco, Bay Area Radio Drama, Palo Alto TheatreWorks, and Fringe Benefits Theatre in Los Angeles, as well as at schools, colleges, and community theatres around the world from Barstow, California to Beijing, China. Publications include *Medusa's Tale* in *Plays in One Act* (Ecco Press) and two short plays for elementary school audiences in *Cootie Shots: Theatrical Inoculations Against Bigotry* (Theatre Communications Group). Two monologues from *Gap* are included in *One on One: The Best Men's Monologues for the 21st*

Century (Applause Books). Scenes from *Gap* and from **Persephone Underground** appear in *DUO! Best Scenes for Two for the 21st century* (Applause Books). As a librettist, Lashof collaborates with British composer James McCarthy; their opera, **Threat Level**, was commissioned by the Scottish National Opera. *Gap*, a short film directed by Ryan Coogler and based on a scene from Carol Lashof's play of the same name, was a finalist in the BET Network's national filmmaking competition, Lens on Talent.

About YouthPLAYS

YouthPLAYS (www.youthplays.com) is a publisher of award-winning professional dramatists and talented new discoveries, each with an original theatrical voice, and all dedicated to expanding the vocabulary of theatre for young actors and audiences. On our website you'll find one-act and full-length plays and musicals for teen and pre-teen (and even college) actors, as well as duets and monologues for competition. Many of our authors' works have been widely produced at high schools and middle schools, youth theatres and other TYA companies, both amateur and professional, as well as at elementary schools, camps, churches and other institutions serving young audiences and/or actors worldwide. Most are intended for performance by young people, while some are intended for adult actors performing for young audiences.

YouthPLAYS was co-founded by professional playwrights Jonathan Dorf and Ed Shockley. It began merely as an additional outlet to market their own works, which included a substantial body of award-winning published and unpublished plays and musicals. Those interested in their published plays were directed to the respective publishers' websites, and unpublished plays were made available in electronic form. But when they saw the desperate need for material for young actors and audiences—coupled with their experience that numerous quality plays for young people weren't finding a home—they made the decision to represent the work of other playwrights as well. Dozens and dozens of authors are now members of the YouthPLAYS family, with scripts available both electronically and in traditional acting editions. We continue to grow as we look for exciting and challenging plays and musicals for young actors and audiences.

About ProduceaPlay.com

Let's put up a play! Great idea! But producing a play takes time, energy and knowledge. While finding the necessary time and energy is up to you, ProduceaPlay.com is a website designed to assist you with that third element: knowledge.

Created by YouthPLAYS' co-founders, Jonathan Dorf and Ed Shockley, ProduceaPlay.com serves as a resource for producers at all levels as it addresses the many facets of production. As Dorf and Shockley speak from their years of experience (as playwrights, producers, directors and more), they are joined by a group of award-winning theatre professionals and experienced teachers from the world of academic theatre, all making their expertise available for free in the hope of helping this and future generations of producers, whether it's at the school or university level, or in community or professional theatres.

The site is organized into a series of major topics, each of which has its own page that delves into the subject in detail, offering suggestions and links for further information. For example, Publicity covers everything from Publicizing Auditions to How to Use Social Media to Posters to whether it's worth hiring a publicist. Casting details Where to Find the Actors, How to Evaluate a Resume, Callbacks and even Dealing with Problem Actors. You'll find guidance on your Production Timeline, The Theater Space, Picking a Play, Budget, Contracts, Rehearsing the Play, The Program, House Management, Backstage, and many other important subjects.

The site is constantly under construction, so visit often for the latest insights on play producing, and let it help make your play production dreams a reality.

More from YouthPLAYS

Persephone Underground by Carol S. Lashof
Drama. 45-60 minutes. 7-20+ females, 2-15 males, 8-10 either (19-45 performers possible).

What would you do if your daughter ran away with the boyfriend from hell? Literally. If you are Demeter, the goddess of the harvest, you have the power to hold the whole earth hostage. One afternoon, Demeter's daughter Persephone is gathering flowers in a field with her mortal friends when she hears an otherworldly melody emanating from a cave. That evening, returning alone to seek the source of the music, she meets a mysterious young demigod who proves to be the nameless son of Hades, the lord of the dead. Drawn to his tales of a world of endless adventures, she follows him. Demeter comes in search of her and demands that she return home, now or never. But when Persephone refuses, Demeter likewise refuses to keep the seasons turning, threatening to destroy the mortal world with drought and famine...

Xtigone by Nambi E. Kelley
Drama. 90-100 minutes. 5-15+ females, 4-15+ males (9-30+ performers possible).

Chicago. Present day. Xtigone's brothers have been killed in drive-by shootings by each other's rival gang. Her powerful uncle calls for the bodies to be buried instead of uncovering the violence in the city streets. In this re-imagining of Sophocles' ***Antigone*** that uses poetry, dance and dialogue that speak with an urban voice, will Xtigone go against his edict and risk death in her quest for her community's truth?

Princess Pigface by Tommy Jamerson
Comedy. 30-40 minutes. 1 female, 2 males, 3-4 either.

When a cruel and selfish king learns that his step-daughter's beauty could be the end to his tyrannical reign, he places a spell on her—cursing her with the face of a pig! Now, Princess Pigface of Hillshire must cross many hills and swim many streams, seeking out acceptance and true love's first kiss. Along the way, she meets a dashingly handsome woodsman who prefers picking flowers to hunting, and comes to learn that true beauty is found within. Told with tongue firmly in cheek, this is a magical fairy tale that both kids and adults should enjoy!

Scheme Space by Claudia Haas
Drama. 25-35 minutes. 5 females, 2 males.

The lives of seven teens collide when an inappropriate photo is put online. Soon, what starts out as a prank spirals out of control. Will this ill-conceived bid for popularity end up destroying friendships and even lives?

A Nutcracker Story by Emily C. A. Snyder
Drama with music. 75-90 minutes. 6+ females, 3+ males, 1-15+ any (10-50+ performers possible).

Drawing from the Tchaikovsky ballet and E. T. A. Hoffman's original tale, *A Nutcracker Story* is part play, part musical, part ballet...and all magic. On Christmas Eve in 1812 Russia, Clara Silberhaus is one sleep away from entering adulthood. But with the last vestiges of war on the horizon, her father's life in danger and a rather irritating—and handsome—young prince come for the festivities, is growing up what Clara really wants? With a little help from her mysterious Uncle Drosselmeier, can Clara dance past her fears (and some troublesome rats) and into a land of newfound courage and a little holiday hope?

Whirligig by John Newman

Drama. 35-45 minutes. 2-21 females, 3-21 males (5-30+ performers possible).

After Brent Bishop gets drunk at a party, causes a car accident, and kills a young woman, the aftermath of his actions overwhelms him. Desperate to find some way to undo the suffering he's caused, Brent accepts the challenge from the victim's mother: build four whirligigs in the corners of the country as memorials to her daughter. As he takes his journey, four individuals he never meets find their lives transformed by the whirligigs he builds. But will the teen be able to forgive himself for an unforgivable mistake and move forward with his life? Also available in a full-length version.

An Avalanche of Murder by Matt Buchanan

Comic Mystery. 75-85 minutes. 8-12 females, 4-7 males (13-16 performers possible).

In this affectionate spoof of old-fashioned murder mysteries, the Hopkins family is trapped in a house by a freak avalanche, and they're dropping like flies. It's up to young Mary and Anthony to figure out who's killing them off one by one—and bragging about it on a dead phone—before there's nobody left.

Between Mars and Me by Rose Helsinger

Drama. 30-40 minutes. 2 gender-flexible performers.

After witnessing the events of 9/11 from his window, Roland withdraws into his apartment and himself, imagining an outside world ravaged by a Martian attack. He won't set foot past his door, instead spending his time reading and researching ways to defeat them. His younger sister tries to bring him back, stopping by every week to bring him food, but as weeks turn into months, will she be able to save him from himself before there isn't anything left of the brother she knew? Winner of the New Voices One-Act Competition for Young Playwrights.